Our Story
for my daughter

Our Story
- for my daughter

Our Story will inspire you to capture the unique story of you and your daughter. Allow an enjoyable hour or two once a year to complete your journal – a great opportunity to reflect on your remarkable relationship.

Our Story helps you to record your amazing family experiences and unrepeatable moments – the growth, development and personality of your daughter, your time together and your emotional journey – your hopes and dreams, the ups and downs and above all, the incredible daughter bond.

On your daughter's 18th birthday she can receive this beautiful hand-written story, a priceless record of your years together, to be shared and treasured forever.

Our Story for

ME

Date of birth …

Place of birth …

Eye color …

Hair color …

Blood group …

My mother's name …

My father's name …

Education …

Date of birth ...

Time of birth ...

Place of birth ...

Who was there ...

Birth weight ...

Hair color ...

Blood group ...

Mother's name ...

Father's name ...

Who you look like ...

"There are two lasting bequests we can
hope to give our children.
One of those is roots, the other is wings."

Hodding Carter

Date

1

A few of
your
favorite
things...

A few of
my
favorite
things...

FOR THE RECORD

Where we live...

Who we live with...

ow I feel about our year together...

Ailments this
year ...

What you are like...

Things you have done and said...

Things that have happened in the world this year...

1

Adventures we have had this year...

Adventures I would love to have with you in the coming year...

My hopes and dreams for the next 12 months…

My predictions of what you will be like when you grow up…

"A mother's arms are more comforting than anyone else's."

Diana, Princess of Wales

Date

2

A few of
your
favorite
things . . .

A few of
my
favorite
things . . .

F O R   T H E   R E C O R D

Where we live . . .

Who we live with . . .

How I feel about our year together...

Ailments this
year ...

What you are like...

Things you have done and said...

Things that have happened in the world this year...

2

Adventures we have had this year...

Adventures I would love to have with you in the coming year...

My hopes and dreams for the next 12 months…

My predictions of what you will be like when you grow up…

"When you are a mother, you are never really alone in your thoughts. A mother always has to think twice, once for herself and once for her child."

Sophia Loren

Date

3

A few of
your
favorite
things . . .

A few of
my
favorite
things . . .

FOR THE RECORD

Where we live . . .

Who we live with . . .

How I feel about our year together...

3

Ailments this
year...

What you are like ...

Things you have done and said...

Things that have happened in the world this year...

3

Adventures we have had this year...

Adventures I would love to have with you in the coming year...

My hopes and dreams for the next 12 months...

My predictions of what you will be like when you grow up...

"Parenting is a stage in life's
journey where the milestones come
about every fifty feet."

Robert Brault

Date

4

A few of
your
favorite
things . . .

A few of
my
favorite
things . . .

FOR THE RECORD

Where we live . . .

Who we live with . . .

How I feel about our year together...

Ailments this year...

4

What you are like...

Things you have done and said...

Things that have happened in the world this year ...

4

Adventures we have had this year...

Adventures I would love to have with you in the coming year...

My hopes and dreams for the next 12 months...

My predictions of what you will be like when you grow up...

"Family life is a bit like a runny apple pie - not perfect but who's complaining."
Author Unknown

Our

Fifth

Year Together

Date

5

A few of
your
favorite
things . . .

A few of
my
favorite
things . . .

FOR THE RECORD

Where we live . . .

Who we live with . . .

How I feel about our year together...

Ailments this year...

What you are like . . .

Things you have done and said…

Things that have happened in the world this year…

Adventures we have had this year...

Adventures I would love to have with you in the coming year...

My hopes and dreams for the next 12 months ...

My predictions of what you will be like when you grow up ...

"Instant availability without
continuous presence is probably
the best role a mother can play."

Lotte Baily

Date

6

A few of
your
favorite
things...

A few of
my
favorite
things...

FOR THE RECORD

Where we live...

Who we live with...

How I feel about our year together...

6

Ailments this year...

What you are like …

Things you have done and said …

Things that have happened in the world this year...

6

Adventures we have had this year...

Adventures I would love to have with you in the coming year...

My hopes and dreams for the next 12 months...

My predictions of what you will be like when you grow up...

"Little girls are cute and small only to Adults. To one another they are not cute. They are life sized."

Margaret Atwood

Date

A few of
your
favorite
things . . .

A few of
my
favorite
things . . .

FOR THE RECORD

Where we live . . .

Who we live with . . .

How I feel about our year together...

Ailments this
year ...

What you are like . . .

Things you have done and said…

Things that have happened in the world this year…

Adventures we have had this year...

Adventures I would love to have with you in the coming year...

My hopes and dreams for the next 12 months...

My predictions of what you will be like when you grow up...

"If you want a baby, have a new one. Don't baby the old one."

Jessamyn West

Our Eighth Year Together

Date

8

A few of
your
favorite
things . . .

A few of
my
favorite
things . . .

FOR THE RECORD

Where we live . . .

Who we live with . . .

How I feel about our year together...

8

Ailments this
year...

8

What you are like…

Things you have done and said…

Things that have happened in the world this year...

8

Adventures we have had this year…

Adventures I would love to have with you in the coming year…

My hopes and dreams for the next 12 months...

My predictions of what you will be like when you grow up...

"A child seldom needs a good
talking to as a good listening to."
Angela Schwindt

Our Ninth Year Together

Date

A few of
your
favorite
things...

A few of
my
favorite
things...

FOR THE RECORD

Where we live...

Who we live with...

How I feel about our year together...

Ailments this
year...

9

9

What you are like ...

...things you have done and said...

...things that have happened in the world this year...

Adventures we have had this year...

Adventures I would love to have with you in the coming year...

My hopes and dreams for the next 12 months...

My predictions of what you will be like when you grow up...

"A child's greatest period of
growth is the month after you have
purchased new school shoes."

Author Unknown

Date

10

A few of your favorite things . . .

A few of my favorite things . . .

FOR THE RECORD

Where we live . . .

Who we live with . . .

How I feel about our year together …

Ailments this
year …

What you are like …

Things you have done and said …

Things that have happened in the world this year...

10

Adventures we have had this year...

Adventures I would love to have with you in the coming year...

My hopes and dreams for the next 12 months …

My predictions of what you will be like when you grow up …

"There are three ways to get things done: do it yourself, employ someone or forbid your children to do it."

Monta Crane

Date

11

A few of your favorite things . . .

A few of my favorite things . . .

FOR THE RECORD

Where we live . . .

Who we live with . . .

How I feel about our year together...

Ailments this
year...

What you are like...

Things you have done and said…

Things that have happened in the world this year…

Adventures we have had this year...

Adventures I would love to have with you in the coming year...

My hopes and dreams for the next 12 months...

My predictions of what you will be like when you grow up...

"One thing a mother must always
save for a rainy day is patience."

Author Unknown

Date

12

A few of
your
favorite
things . . .

A few of
my
favorite
things . . .

FOR THE RECORD

Where we live . . .

Who we live with . . .

How I feel about our year together...

Ailments this year...

12

What you are like...

Things you have done and said...

Things that have happened in the world this year ...

12

Adventures we have had this year...

Adventures I would love to have with you in the coming year...

My hopes and dreams for the next 12 months...

My predictions of what you will be like when you grow up...

"It is the little things in common that make relationships enjoyable... but it is the little differences that make them interesting."

Todd Ruthman

Date

13

A few of
your
favorite
things . . .

A few of
my
favorite
things . . .

FOR THE RECORD

Where we live . . .

Who we live with . . .

How I feel about our year together...

Ailments this year...

What you are like...

Things you have done and said…

Things that have happened in the world this year…

Adventures we have had this year...

Adventures I would love to have with you in the coming year...

My hopes and dreams for the next 12 months…

My predictions of what you will be like when you grow up…

"Where parents do too much for
their children, the children will not
do much for themselves."

Elbert Hubbard

Date

14

A few of your favorite things . . .

A few of my favorite things . . .

FOR THE RECORD

Where we live . . .

Who we live with . . .

14

How I feel about our year together...

Ailments this year...

14

What you are like …

Things you have done and said …

Things that have happened in the world this year...

Adventures we have had this year...

Adventures I would love to have with you in the coming year...

My hopes and dreams for the next 12 months…

My predictions of what you will be like when you grow up…

"At fourteen you don't need
sickness or death for tragedy."

Jessamyn West

Date

15

A few of
your
favorite
things . . .

A few of
my
favorite
things . . .

FOR THE RECORD

Where we live . . .

Who we live with . . .

How I feel about our year together . . .

Ailments this
year . . .

What you are like...

Things you have done and said…

Things that have happened in the world this year…

Adventures we have had this year...

Adventures I would love to have with you in the coming year...

My hopes and dreams for the next 12 months...

My predictions of what you will be like when you grow up...

"Being a mother means your heart is no longer yours, it wanders wherever your children do."

Author Unknown

Date

16

A few of
your
favorite
things...

A few of
my
favorite
things...

FOR THE RECORD

Where we live...

Who we live with...

How I feel about our year together ...

Ailments this year ...

What you are like...

Things that you have done and said...

Things that have happened in the world this year...

Adventures we have had this year...

Adventures I would love to have with you in the coming year...

My hopes and dreams for the next 12 months...

My predictions of what you will be like when you grow up...

"To an adolescent, there is nothing in the world more embarrassing than a parent."

Dave Barry

Date

17

A few of
your
favorite
things...

A few of
my
favorite
things...

FOR THE RECORD

Where we live ...

Who we live with ...

How I feel about our year together...

Ailments this year...

What you are like...

Things you have done and said...

Things that have happened in the world this year...

Adventures we have had this year...

Adventures I would love to have with you in the coming year...

My hopes and dreams for the next 12 months...

My predictions of what you will be like when you grow up...

"Adolescence is perhaps Nature's way of preparing parents to welcome the empty nest."

Karen Savage and Patricia Adams

Our
Eighteenth
Year Together

18

A few of
your
favorite
things . . .

A few of
my
favorite
things . . .

FOR THE RECORD

Where we live . . .

Who we live with . . .

How I feel about our year together...

Ailments this
year...

What you are like …

Things you have done and said …

Things that have happened in the world this year...

18

Adventures we have had this year ...

Adventures I would love to have with you in the coming year...

My hopes and dreams for our futures are ...

"When you have brought up kids,
there are memories you store
directly in your tear ducts."

Robert Brault

What I love about you...

Some words of advice for the next stage of your life are…

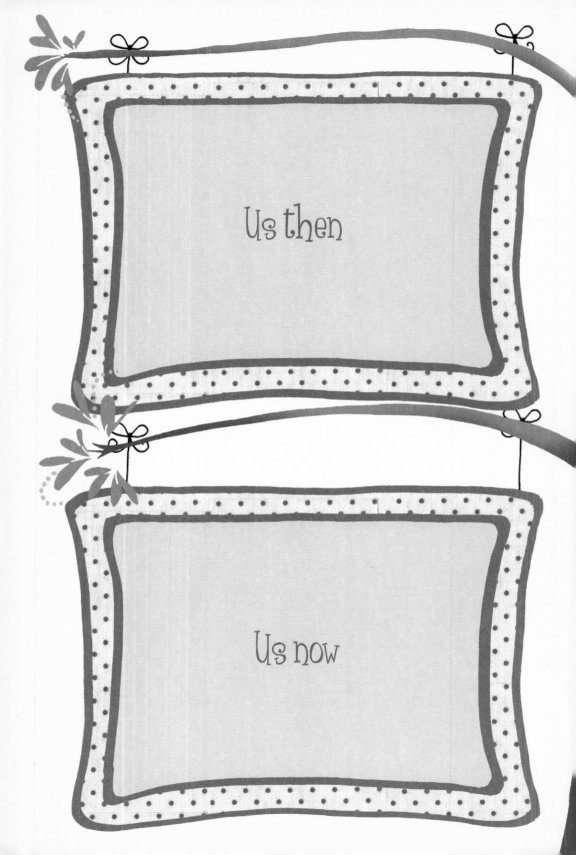

Us then

Us now

"Home is where we tie one
end of the thread of life."

Martin Buxbaum

Our Story – for my daughter

First published (US version) by *from you to me* limited, April 2013

Every effort has been made to credit all quoted material correctly; should there by any errors or omissions in this respect we apologise and shall be pleased to make the appropriate changes in any future edition.

Designed by Helen Stephens and Lucy Tapper.

Printed and bound in China by Imago.

This paper is manufactured from pulp sourced from forests that are legally and sustainably managed.

For more information please contact:
from you to me ltd
The Cottage Suite, The Old Brewery, Wine Street,
Bradford on Avon, BA15 1NS, England, UK.

Email: mail@fromyoutome.com

For tips, information and help on completing your journal please go to
www.fromyoutome.com/share

Published by from you to me ltd

from you to me Journals of a Lifetime*
Dear Mom
Dear Dad
Dear Grandma
Dear Grandpa
Dear Daughter
Dear Son
Dear Sister
Dear Brother
Dear Friend

*Also available to personalize online at www.fromyoutome.us

Home & Garden Journals
Cooking up Memories

Parent & Child
Bump to Birthday – pregnancy & first year journal
Our Story – for my daughter
Our Story – for my son

Christmas Memories
Christmas Present, Christmas Past

Anniversary & Relationship
Love Stories

All titles are available at gift and book shops or www.fromyoutome.us

Follow us on Facebook and Twitter and read our blogs at
http://fromyoutomeltd.blogspot.co.uk

for each and every child

www.fromyoutome.us